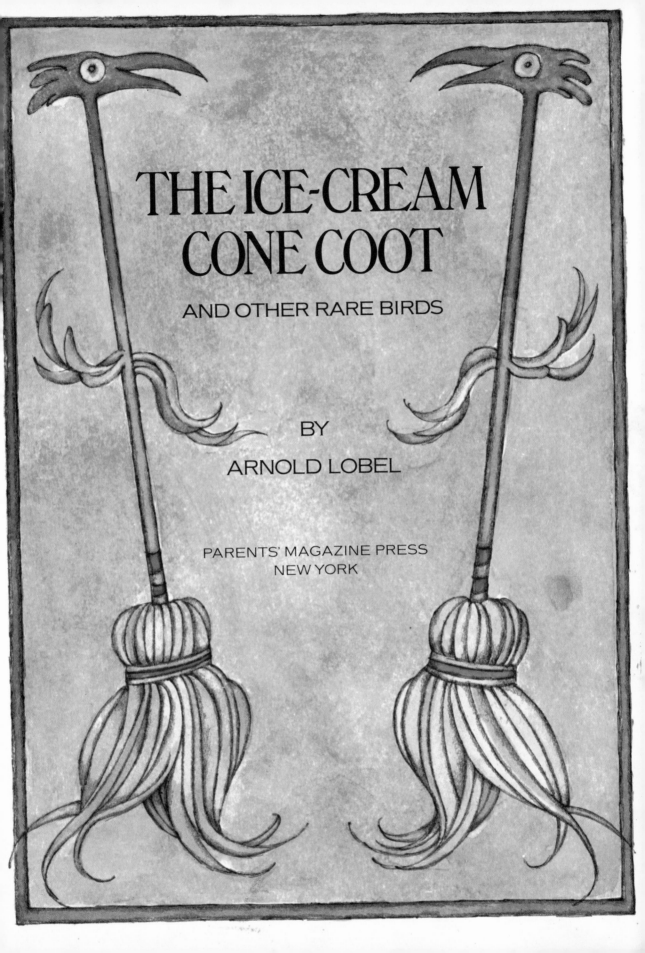

THE ICE-CREAM CONE COOT

AND OTHER RARE BIRDS

BY

ARNOLD LOBEL

PARENTS' MAGAZINE PRESS
NEW YORK

Many of the birds in this book have previously
appeared in HUMPTY DUMPTY'S MAGAZINE.

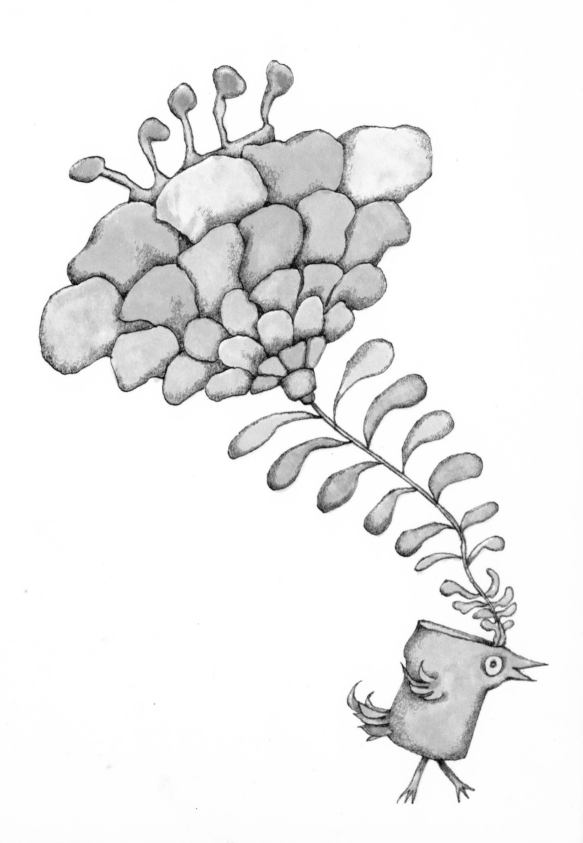

The Birds Inside this Book

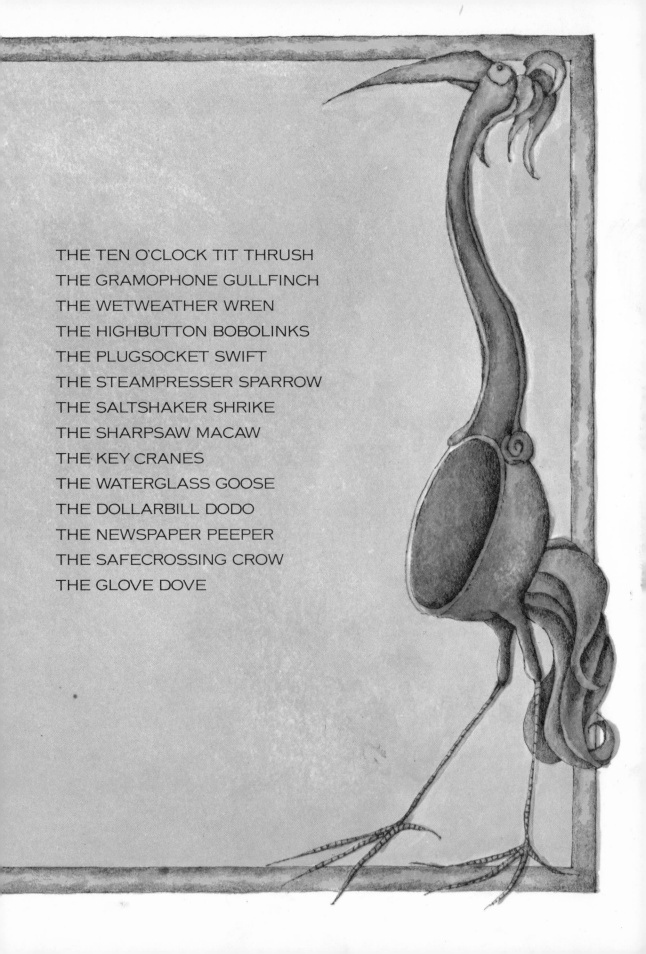

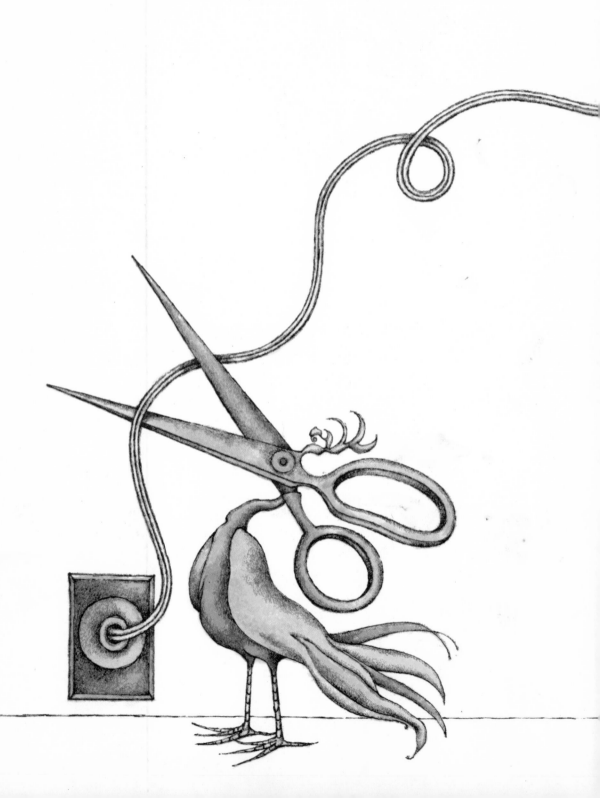

All the birds inside this book
Are very strange and rare,
And if you travel to the zoo
You will not find them there.
Don't look for them in nature books,
In parks or pet shop cages,
The Drippet, Piffle and the rest
Live only on these pages.

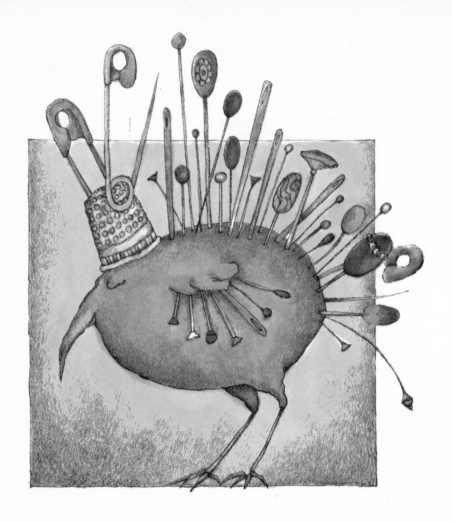

All ladies agree, this bird is worth knowing.
The Pincushion Piffle will help with the sewing.

When the Drippet
Runs along the street
He leaves little puddles
So watch your feet.

For writing a list or maybe a letter
The Pencilkeet Parrot could hardly be better.

Vanilla and chocolate, lemon and lime.
The Ice-Cream Cone Coot is a treat anytime.

This bird will tip his empty head.
He'll ask you please to fill it.
Pour tea into the Cupadee
And take care not to spill it.

The Shuttercluck will never sing, nor will he ever fly.
But he can take your picture when he clicks his big round eye.

The dirtiest bird is the Garbage Canary.
He lives in conditions quite unsanitary.

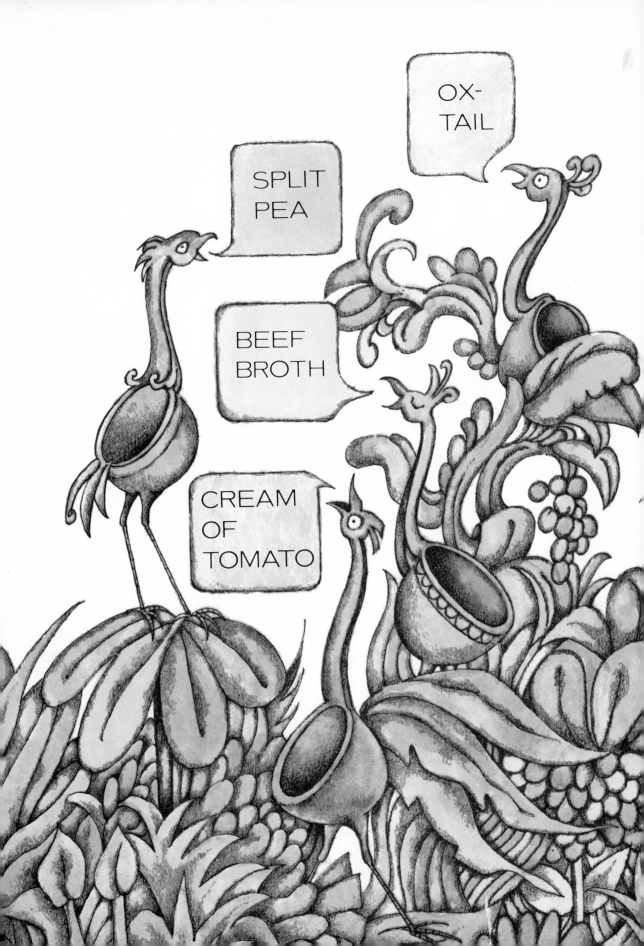

Down in hot jungles, steaming and dark,
Hear the loud calls of the Soupladle Lark.

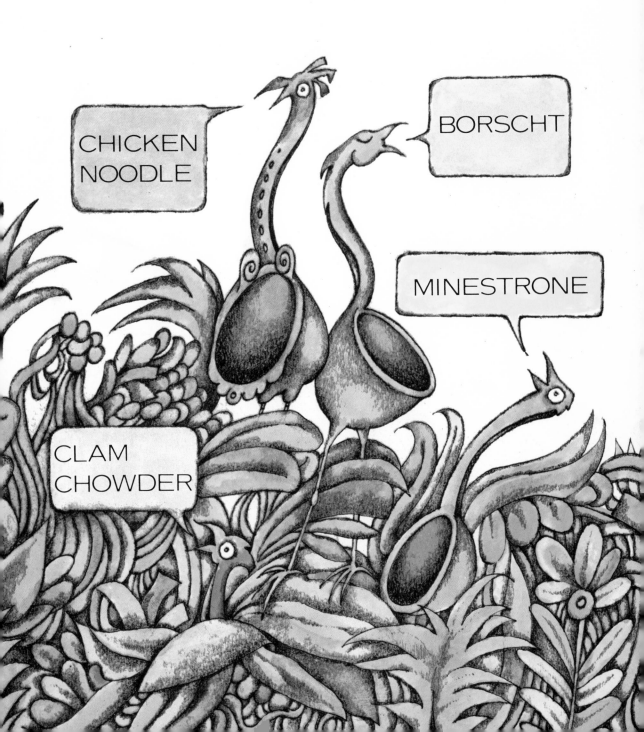

I do not trust the Jackknife Niffy.
He could swoop down and cut off your nose in a jiffy.

All the Buttonbeaks are small.
Their shape is neatly round.
Look down upon your shirtfront.
That's where they can be found.

The Milkbottle Midge is a bird highly prized.
He is friendly and round and homogenized.

The Cutitup Snippit makes holes in the trees.
He clips all the leaves off and does it with ease.

Each day you must water your Flowerpot Plume.
The buds in his bird brain are certain to bloom.

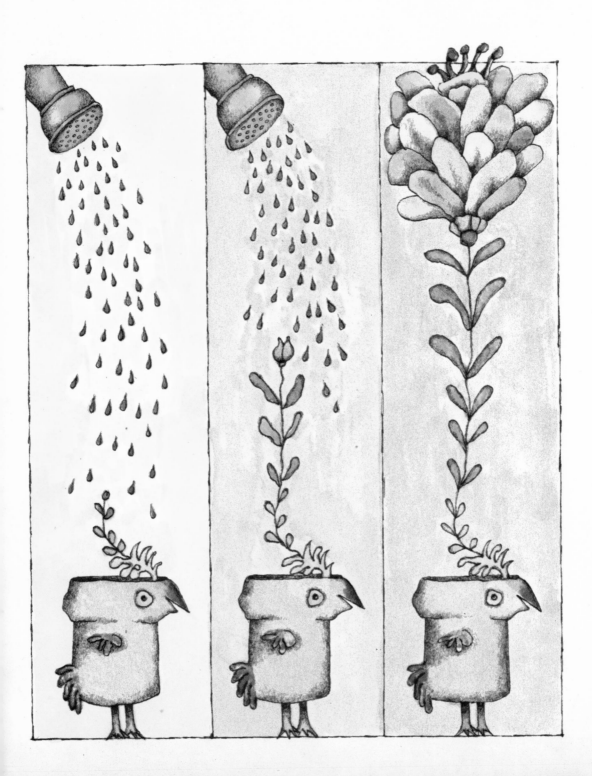

The Broomwhisk is a well-known bird
And one you may have seen.
Your mother uses him each day
To keep her household clean.

The Ten O'clock Tit Thrush takes to the skies.
He soars high above us, and time really flies.

The Gramophone Gullfinch will beautifully sing.
Just put on a record and wind up the spring.

Showers and storms please the Wetweather Wren.
When the cloudburst is over, he flies home again.

These Highbutton Bobolinks
Croon to the night.
One fits the left foot,
One fits the right.

The Plugsocket Swift is a high voltage bird.
His head is a light bulb, or so I have heard.

Ironing clothes will make them lie flat.
The Steampresser Sparrow is good for just that.

The Saltshaker Shrike
Has the shakes for good reasons.
You'll love him when tasting
The food that he seasons.

The Sharpsaw Macaw
Is ever so gentle.
Those teeth that you see
Are just ornamental.

Over our heads the Key Cranes are flocking,
Looking for doors that might need unlocking.

The Waterglass Goose
Can't be dropped on the floor.
If this one should break
There just aren't any more.

The Dollarbill Dodo is easy to spot.
He is made of green paper and worth quite a lot.

Instead of fine feathers as most other birds,
The Newspaper Peeper is covered with words.

BIRD SEED PRICES UP

A good friend to know
Is the Safecrossing Crow.
The red eye means stop,
The green eye means go.

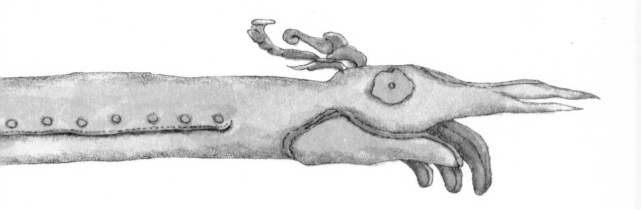

And here we see the Glove Dove, poised in lofty flight.
He doesn't know that pointing is considered impolite.

Yes, all the birds inside this book
Are very strange and rare,
And I repeat, it would be hard
To find them anywhere.
So do not search your neighborhood
With cage or trap or net,
For not a single boy or girl
Has ever caught one yet.

ARNOLD LOBEL has been both an author and illustrator in the field of children's books ever since his graduation from Pratt Institute. The best-known books he has written and illustrated include A Zoo for Mister Muster, selected by the New York Times as one of the ten best books of the year in 1963, A Holiday for Mister Muster, Prince Bertram the Bad, and most recently, Frog and Toad Are Friends. His artwork can also be seen in three books on the Parents' list: Junk Day on Juniper Street, The Magic Spectacles, and Miss Suzy.

Mr. Lobel makes his home in Brooklyn, New York, with his wife, Anita Lobel, also an author and illustrator of children's books, and their two children, Adrianne and Adam.